PASSING ON A TRADITION OF TEACHING

A NATURALISTIC STUDY OF YOGA THERAPY

AT THE

KRISHNAMACHARYA YOGA MANDIRAM

BY JANE W. YOUNG, PH.D.

Copyright © 2006 Jane W. Young
Published by: KRISHNAMACHARYA YOGA MANDIRAM
31 (old No: 13) Fourth Cross Street
R K Nagar
Chennai 600 028 India

ISBN: 81-87847-26-3

Cover Design : Kausthub Desikachar

Photo on page 40 by Masakatsu Kinoshita
All other photos © Kausthub Desikachar

Printed by : Vignesha Printers, Chennai 600 005. Phone +91.44.28419352

Publisher's Note:
Most of the information in this book has been obtained through personal interviews conducted by the author and observations made by her co-researchers. Excerpts from the interviews have been reproduced verbatim to substantiate the author's interpretations. Direct quotations appear as indented blocks within the narrative.

The author invites dialog from readers, and can be contacted at jyoung@dnet.net

I dedicate this work to the memory of
Martin G. Pierce who opened the door for me.

TABLE OF CONTENTS

continued on next page...

Table of Contents (Continued)

ACKNOWLEDGEMENTS

Many individuals have given their generous support to this project. I express my gratitude to:

Dorothy Conlon, my co-researcher, for her astute observations and reflections on many therapy sessions at the KYM, her calm and thorough prodding of the unfolding analysis, her careful reading of the manuscript as it progressed, and her enduring encouragement;

Kate Holcombe, co-researcher, for selflessly contributing her personal notes and records to the body of data, for exploring with me the meanings of our observations, and for inspiring me with her dedication to learning and teaching;

The participating teachers at the KYM, all of whom freely granted the interviews and so enriched my understanding of what it means to be a yoga teacher and therapist;

The administrative staff of the KYM for fixing the time slots and arranging the spaces for the interviews, and doing it all with perfect cooperation and good cheer;

Rosemary Antze, Jim Kolarik, Rachel Krishnan and Virginia Wise for reading and giving insightful feedback on the manuscript;

The KYM Publications staff for facilitating the revision process with such care and professionalism;

John Young, my husband, who never runs out of patience;

and T. K. V. Desikachar, my teacher, whose vision, wisdom and energy inspire and support all those who participate in passing on this tradition of teaching.

CHAPTER 1

"IT'S A MIRACLE!"

In 1985 my seventy year old mother accompanied me on my second trip to Madras, India to study with my teacher, T. K. V. Desikachar. Mother had little attraction to yoga. To the contrary, she was mildly annoyed at my enduring interest and hoped that I would find something more substantial to do with my life than teaching yoga. She asked to take this trip with me; I believe she wanted to avoid eleven weeks of worrying about my traveling and living alone in India.

On the flight over, Mother casually mentioned that she might take some yoga lessons while in Madras. It would be something for her to do while I was busy with my studies. But, she proclaimed, she would not practice yoga other than during her lessons, and she certainly would not do it when she returned home. After the long and wearying flight—South Carolina to New York to London to Delhi and finally to Madras—we went to bed exhausted. A few hours later, Mother woke with a severe headache. She spent the next day in bed, nauseated and grimacing in pain. The eleven weeks supply of Tylenol filling a corner of her bag was little help.

We settled into our quarters in the city and I began my lessons with Desikachar. I asked him if Mother could take some lessons with one of the teachers at his institute, the Krishnamacharya Yoga Mandiram. He assigned her to Laksmi, a young woman whom I sensed was a bit of a feminist, married to an airline pilot. I went with Mother to the Mandiram and sat on the porch while she had her first private lesson. When she came out she was all smiles and said, as though surprised, "Well, I do feel better." In her hand she had a sheet of graph paper with stick figures drawn by Laksmi, illustrating the postures she was to practice before her next lesson. On the way back to our apartment, Mother chatted perkily. A few minutes into her lesson, Laksmi had asked thoughtfully, "Do you have headaches?" Mother told her yes, for many years she woke most mornings with a headache. Her doctor had offered no solution; her dentist had ruled out a suspected temporal mandibular joint dysfunction. But Laksmi's quick reply was, "We'll take care of those headaches." Mother was amazed at her teacher's confidence.

Mother did her practice each morning without fail and with no complaint. She did slow, simple arm movements, both seated and standing, and some gentle movements on the floor to stretch her low back. Laksmi had emphasized the importance of paying attention to her breathing throughout the practice and making her exhalations long and smooth. She ended her practice sitting on a stool, counting twelve relaxed breaths.

Her lessons were two times a week, gradually including other postures and breathing exercises to relax her neck and back and to develop her ability to breathe out slowly and smoothly. Mother looked forward to her lessons, and her admiration for Laksmi grew. But her greatest delight was that she did not have even one headache after her first lesson. People we met during our first week in India, when seeing her again, commented that she looked different. Her face had changed and so had her voice. Later, telling her friends that she did yoga and got rid of her chronic headaches, she exclaimed, "It's a miracle!"

Seventeen years later my mother still does her morning yoga practice. Occasionally she has broken her routine and stopped practicing. According to her, after about a week the headaches return, giving her incentive to get back to her daily practice. From time to time, she has ventured into a group yoga class at her retirement community or in an Elderhostel program and consequently inserted new postures into her routine. Each of those instances has been troublesome. When she complains of her neck hurting, I question her and learn that she has picked up inappropriate postures, randomly sequenced in her practice. I remind her that not everything called yoga is good for her.

In 1985, we didn't use the term, "yoga therapy." What guided Laksmi's work with Mother was the same thing that guided her work with any other student. Everything she taught her was chosen specifically for her, based on her needs and her limitations. Laksmi drew from classic yoga postures and techniques but adapted each of them so that they would be useful to Mother and she would be comfortable doing them. Her manner with

Mother was just right, and the good feeling seemed to be mutual. I remember that in one of my few conversations with her, Laksmi commented, "Your mother is a wonderful woman." I felt that in her assured, professional way, she truly cared about her student.

Today the term, yoga therapy, is common parlance among yoga teachers, in yoga publications, and on internet sites numbering in the thousands. Yoga teachers debate the definition and implications of yoga therapy (Feuerstein, 2000, 2001). They address these and other questions: How is yoga therapy different from any other yoga that supports health and healing? Does the term suggest separating the physical techniques of yoga from its spiritual aspects? And more pragmatic for individuals in the business of teaching, does holism in yoga therapy preclude its acceptance as a reimbursable (by health insurance) treatment?

While yoga teachers in the west, at least, struggle with the meanings and the economics of yoga therapy, much of the general public has developed quite an appetite for the health-giving and healing capacities of yoga. Health professionals today, unlike a generation ago, are not reticent about encouraging their patients to take up yoga to reduce stress and alleviate various aches and pains. The increasingly visible field of integrative medicine supports mind-body therapies such as yoga, but at the same time, emphasizes the need to accumulate empirical evidence of their efficacy (Walach, Jonas, and Lewith, 2002).

Yoga teachers aspiring to do yoga therapy, whatever their understanding of the term, feel pressure to validate claims that yoga can heal. The need to produce evidence of yoga's effectiveness and safety as therapy is indeed real. But it is difficult to evaluate what has no operational definition. Just what it is that we do when we say we are doing yoga therapy? On what basis do we decide what to teach when a person with back pain or headache or anxiety—or all of those and more—comes to us for help? Why do particular yoga techniques appear to work for some individuals but not for others? Even if we are skilled in our assessments and ability to design a therapeutic practice, how do we get the student to do what is necessary, that is, to practice on a regular basis?

These are salient questions, perhaps more salient than the questions, "Can yoga heal, and, if so, how can we prove it?" This study does not address the efficacy of yoga therapy, or what *asanas* work for what problem. Rather, this study examines the practice of teaching yoga for purposes of therapy. Its focus is on the processes that constitute this encounter between yoga teacher and student, rather than on the results of a particular intervention. The findings of this study are based on narrative data derived from interviews of teachers at the Krishnamacharya Yoga Mandiram in Chennai (formerly Madras), India in December 1999 and January 2000. The methods used in collecting and analyzing data for the study are given in the appendix.

The processes of any human enterprise are always variable and laden with subjective input and meaning. Processes are often difficult to identify, difficult to measure, and difficult to explain. Moreover, the details of process may seem so ordinary that they do not capture our attention. This study purposefully looked for details given by teachers at the Krishnamacharya Yoga Mandiram describing their own experiences and perspectives on yoga therapy. The teachers' narratives were examined using qualitative methods, and were restructured according to themes derived from the entire body of data. These themes, elucidating the processes of yoga therapy, are developed in Chapters 2, 3, 4, and 5. Chapter 6 summarizes the findings of the study and discusses their validity.

The Study Site

The Krishnamacharya Yoga Mandiram (KYM) in Chennai, India was the site of this study. Established in 1976 for the purpose of implementing the teachings of T. Krishnamacharya, the KYM is a public charitable trust (not-for-profit organization) recognized by the Department of Family Health and Welfare of the state of Tamil Nadu, India. T. Krishnamacharya (1888-1989) is recognized for his vast knowledge of yoga and other Indian philosophies, and his ability to apply that knowledge to the rapidly changing values and lifestyles of modern times. A firm believer in the therapeutic and healing potential of yoga, Krishnamacharya made it his life's work to heal people by adapting yoga to suit their individual needs. With a staff of over 30 teachers trained in this tradition, the KYM is unique in its preservation of the core teachings of yoga and the application of those teachings for purposes of healing.

The KYM program includes Yoga Studies, Yoga Therapy, Research, Publications, and Yoga for Children. Yoga Studies include training programs and workshops offered to both Indian and international students, as well as seminars conducted in the community and throughout the world. Typically, one or more medical doctors and one or more doctoral level psychologists are among the KYM staff.

Yoga Therapy has been a vital component of the KYM program since its inception in 1976. Thousands of individuals have come to the KYM for help with a wide variety of physical, psychological, and emotional problems. The student is first met by a senior consultant who assesses his or her requirements, assesses the magnitude of the problem for which therapy is sought, and determines the course best suited to that individual. The student is then assigned a teacher, who, on a one-to-one basis, guides the practice based on the consultant's directions. Senior teachers continue to monitor the course given by the teacher to ensure that the course remains appropriate for the changes occurring in the student's condition and circumstances.

The vision for the Krishnamacharya Yoga Mandiram came from T. K. V. Desikachar, son and student of Krishnamacharya for the last 30 years of his father's life. Desikachar's teaching and personal guidance have been the basis for all the teaching and training programs offered at the KYM.

CHAPTER 2

TAILORING THE TEACHING
TO THE INDIVIDUAL STUDENT

Four major themes were derived from the interviews with teachers doing yoga therapy at the Krishnamacharya Yoga Mandiram. The first and most fundamental theme is that whatever is taught to the student is uniquely tailored to that individual. Therefore the teaching must take into account multiple aspects of the individual including physical and mental health, age, occupation, culture, and gender, as well as the student's ability to comprehend. Because of this unique orientation to the individual, yoga therapy cannot be prescriptive. In other words, a particular ailment, for instance, back pain, does not determine the course that is given. As explained by one informant,

> What happens is that the back pain is manifested as one portion of an individual with a lot of problems together. . . . The back pain is not a simple back pain. . . . But let me tell you one thing. We never treat a back pain, because we understand that in therapy, you treat an individual totally.

Tailoring the teaching to the student encompasses several constituent themes. These are: (a) The initial consultation provides the basis for establishing an individualized course, (b) The teaching is done one-to-one, taking into account the unique characteristics of the individual, (c) The course begins at a level appropriate to this student at this time, no matter how rudimentary, and (d) The courses tend to be both focused and efficient, often using quite simple techniques.

The Initial Consultation

"Treating an individual totally" requires a careful assessment of the student. At the KYM, this begins when the student first meets one of the consultants on duty at the time of his initial appointment. The consultant's first responsibility is to put the new student at ease and to lay the foundation for further work. During this first meeting, the student begins to form his attitude toward the practice.

> I think the consultant is the most important step in the whole thing. Because the student is being introduced to the concept of yoga for the first time. So we need to assure them that it is nothing so difficult to practice, or that [it will not be] such a time constraint—not a one-hour program. . . . So the biggest job of the consultant, I believe, is to relax the student. We need to do this even before we deal with a headache or a backache.

The consultant is also laying the groundwork for helping the student experience yoga as "more than an exercise." Yoga should help the students "feel for themselves, study themselves, make improvements for themselves."

Typically, the new student fills out a brief form including notes on present health problems, current treatment and medication, and past health history. The consultant also asks for the student's own view on the nature of the problem. He is attempting to understand both the physical and mental dimensions of the situation.

> When the person comes in, we ask them to explain what they want as a relief. "What is the problem . . . . in your own words, apart from what you have written here? You have written back pain." You know, the public is so much aware now. They talk about L-4, L-5, C-5 . . . . So we allow them to talk in medical terms. But then we say, "Okay, let me understand, how does the pain come, does it come often, when does it come, does it come every time . . . ?" And so, slowly, the link between the back and the mind is brought out. They come out slowly, and we get a lot of ideas. It could be premenstrual; it could be a work situation, a highly stressed traveling executive, a person who stands too much on the floor. But they come and they talk, and we get into the mental portion slowly.

A teacher recalled her own experience as a student coming to the KYM for treatment of her asthma. She was impressed that the teachers took into account so much more than her asthma symptoms.

I came here, and the way they received me, the way they examined me, was totally different. I thought, something is happening for once. . . . Here, they made me sit comfortably, made me feel at ease, and they never asked for the big volumes of reports. They asked me to say a few words about my suffering. . . . They made me think for the first time [about] what is happening.

During this first encounter, the consultant gets a great deal of information by observation. He is trying to understand the problem identified by the student and to ascertain what else may relate to the problem.

Most of the input we get is from our own observation. Even the way you sit, the way you position your head when you are talking. . . . is there tension in the shoulder? As we are talking, we look at your eyes . . . . if there is anxiety in your system, if your palms are sweating. . . . Sometimes an over anxious person never stops talking. So we know an underlying thing is there other than their symptomatic expression of a headache or a back pain or a stomach pain. There is something more to it.

If the student talks little about situations that may be behind overt symptoms, the consultant gives more time to the conversation. If still the student says little, the consultant informs the teacher, "There is something more to the story that we have to see."

Usually most of them open up with the consultants, even after 15 minutes. If not, they will with the teacher in the first or second sitting. And then the teacher and the consultant work together.

Identifying the cause of the problem is not particularly easy and should not be over-simplified.

The cause quite often cannot be immediately seen, but we try to find out. We derive slowly, one by one. We start with the physical. Sometimes we ask them to breathe in and breathe out, and then we may find out. . . . But it is very difficult to find out the root cause. Actually there is no one simple root cause. Even the root cause is [complicated] in the sense that it is more than one. If you want to make it simple, it is mind, that's all. But it's too simple understanding it that way.

The consultant tries to ascertain what is needed in the practice, as well as what should be avoided at the beginning.

We ask them to do certain postures to see if the alignment is alright, some asymmetrical posture . . . . we see how their body moves . . . . We ask them to do some breaths; we take their pulse before and after the breathing. So this kind of clinical information gives the teacher an idea of where to start and what not to do. Because it would be very risky to start with certain postures. So the "don'ts" first. And in certain cases, only a relaxation technique will help the person to start with.

Never is the course designed for the student simply prescriptive according to a diagnosis. Factors in addition to the diagnosis must be taken in to account.

We cannot just prescribe this *asana* for this problem. It is not possible. . . . Even though two persons have the same back pain, their courses [will be different] according to their physical structure. For one person, the stiffness will be in the back. Another person will feel it in the neck. So the counter pose may be different. The course will change.

The consultant establishes a priority for the student's first course, orienting it to the problem that is causing the difficulty. Only after the condition is stabilized and the immediate symptoms are addressed will the practice focus on strengthening the entire system. For instance, sometimes all the postures in the initial course will be lying postures, as in treating hypertension. After the blood pressure has been lowered satisfactorily the course will include other appropriate postures.

The consultant may see the problem differently from what the student has identified as the primary problem. But she must take the student's concerns into account.

The clinical diagnosis may say there is a swelling in the kneecap or in the ankle—these are things that the student is looking at. They want to see something happening to the areas that are affected. So we have to pay attention to that so that we are able to do something for it.

Recognizing the importance of hope and a positive attitude, the consultant assures the student that he can be helped. But she emphasizes that the student must give the teacher feedback on what he experiences in his practice. It is also important to allow time for results to occur.

I make it a point during consultations to reassure the student that they will find a definite improvement, but only if they are willing to cooperate and open up with us and speak what they feel, even if there is not improvement. . . . I insist that if they don't find improvement for the problem, they must not drop the program because of that. I tell them, "It only means changing the program a little more to suit you. But we are not magicians here. We have to learn to work with your body and your mind. So you have to give us time to work". . . . It is not a one week program, but definitely they will see a benefit in the long term. It is not like they take a tablet and immediately see some effect.

The practice designed for the student must be practical from his standpoint. It must not be uncomfortable or require more time than can be reasonably given. Thus the practice may be quite brief, but the consultant insists on daily practice.

I tell them, "Even if you are spending ten minutes, that's alright. But spend the ten minutes every day." We do not tell them half an hour or forty minutes to begin with. Because these days we do find people have a lot of constraints for time.

Neither does the consultant insist on a certain time of day for practice.

We have no restriction [such as] practice only in the morning, or on an empty stomach. Do the practice any time you want. All you need to do is see that you do not have a full stomach. So we give them all kinds of liberties these days.

Working One-to-One

Once the consultant has determined the initial direction of the course, she assigns a teacher who will teach him individually. The choice of teacher for this student is not happenstance but a "part intuitive and part rational" decision.

[When they assign a teacher] they have so many things to look into. . . . When a person comes here and meets me as a teacher, as soon as he sees me he must have some confidence. And there must be some good interaction between us. . . . Unless he comes with good confidence, I don't think the course will help him.

The assigned teacher follows the consultant's directions concerning what postures and breathing practices will comprise the course. Always, the postures are "modified according to the person's requirement." For example, the individual may be instructed to bend his elbows rather than keep the arms straight, or to bend over and touch the seat of a chair. Within a few days, the first practice is checked, and appropriate changes are made.

> We have a review class, probably within five days, to find out if the *asanas* that we have given him have done him any harm. It is too early to say if he has derived any good out of it, but it should not do him any harm. . . . For example, one student I observed had a pain when he was raising his arms while lying down. It was stretching his back [too much] and it was causing him pain. So after he started doing it, after four days, he said, "I have terrible pain. I don't want to do it." So then we had him bend his legs so that the stretch would be less. He was doing it flat, so we had him bend his knees.

One-to-one teaching allows the teacher to develop a rapport with the student. This feeling between the two helps the student trust the practice even though it may not be what was expected. One teacher recalled her own early skepticism when she was a new student at the KYM, coming for therapy.

> [I was given] simple *asanas* like arm movement and *tadasana.* Inside me, I was not very convinced that this is going to work because I had done much more than this [in yoga classes elsewhere]. But it seemed to be very organized. They would teach me and give me this sheet every week and I was supposed to meet her [teacher] at a particular time. . . . And she would talk and ask me all kinds of things about my life and so on. And that kind of established a rapport, so it was something I looked forward to.

In their interactions with the student, teachers continue to reinforce the positive attitude that was aimed at in the initial consultation. They are "not blindly saying, this will happen or that will happen," but they give hope. Even though the ailment may be incurable, the teacher knows that the student's practice can strengthen his ability to face the situation.

Over time the teacher learns more about the student's greater life situation. The problem for which help is sought is rarely isolated from other parts of the individual's life, either in cause or effect. The developing practice addresses more than the obvious symptoms of the problem.

> You see, the teacher's job is not just to give the course. So we [ask] "What is it you do from morning to evening, what is your mode of travel . . . ?" We have to get such

I
L
o
v
e

y
o
4

..... So from the small tips to the larger stuff, planning their course, when
.rselves with the day-to-day activity of the person, then they start talking
.essures and what happened in the house . . . . and what is causing them
.ay, the tension is going to [increase her pain]. So what am I going to do
.sion? The [course] is going to revolve around her tension rather than any
. for her arthritis. . . . We have to help them deal with themselves in their life
. Unless we do that, we have not accomplished anything. It is not as simple as
.ramming something on a sheet of paper.

ere the Student Is

Early in their training, teachers learn to appreciate the necessity of starting where
the student is. For new teachers it may be a revelation to see just how elementary this
starting place needs to be. One teacher, also a physician, described a case from his medical
practice.

He had some problems with a part of his lungs that was removed. Added to that, he
had severe asthma. He could not speak three or four sentences without having to cough
and spit out. He could not walk even 100 meters without taking rest. He was 52 years
old. So I gave him some antibiotic and asked him to come after a week. He followed the
instruction nicely; he came after a week, and he had exactly the same condition. Not an
inch of improvement.

So I got [Desikachar's] instruction and I gave him his first [yoga] course. In his
next class, he said that after practice of this one, the cough is not much. He has to spit
out but there is a definite improvement. Then only it struck me. We have to start where the
man is, and that man's place is very, very rudimentary, not even inhalation and exhalation.
You have to take him from his place to a little more comfortable place, step by step. Our
practices [typically] may be movement and breathing with the mental involvement. But
with him, not even breathing. His breathing is very shallow; part of the lung is removed.
Phlegm is in his chest. No point in coordinating breath and movement.

So some simple movement like this (showed partial arm raises), simple
sound—say, "mah"—that's all. Even that sound will not be very long. So from that place
we just guided him to a little better place. . . . After some five or six weeks he was able to
do some breathing—inhale and exhale. And he was free from his frequent spitting also,
and the breathing improved.

Even students without severe physical problems require adaptations of classic postures. A relatively new teacher stated that he has taught seventeen students and "not a single one have I taught in the traditional way. It has all been adaptation."

It may have nothing to do with the limbs. They are not able to bend. I think that is basic to every person working in an office or in a blue collar job. They are not able to bend or stretch. So in that way they are not able to make full use of their limbs. Consequently they are not aware of their breathing. They are not aware of what thoughts are happening, what is concentration, what they are working on—nothing. So in the traditional sense, they are not healthy.

Once the yoga practice begins at the appropriate level, the progression is step-by-step, with each step building on the progress made in earlier steps. This progression cannot be programmed in advance. The rate and direction of progress is always an individual matter.

I had a college student, 19 years old, with back pain and headache. [Normally] for 19 years old, general person, you can give *surya namaskar, vinyasa* . . . . But I had her just lie down and I gave her mild lying postures. At her second class, she [reported] that for the past week, the back pain came only once, and headache very mildly once or twice. She came for her third class. The back pain is fully over, so I gave her some forward bending. She wanted to get [weight] off her tummy. So slowly I started from the lying posture to the standing posture.

Tailoring yoga to the individual also includes gauging how much the particular student can assimilate. It means not to overwhelm him with too many postures and too many instructions.

There are certain students who have some psychological problems—that, and it's difficult for them to keep focused on something. So the instructions, how we design the course, should not burden them. They should be able to do what has been given.

Interviewer: Do you mean, make it simple enough?

Yes, initially. Let them get into something. Let them slowly understand. Then, slowly we can move on. It is something new for them, and they have to understand. Those things that are simple may not be possible for people with psychological problems. So we have to tell them again and again. If even then it is not possible, we can teach them breathing. So that way we can help them. But we have to make the right communication in making them understand.

Some students are "quick on the uptake" and easily grasp the coordination of movement with breath. For others, the first attempts to think about whether they are inhaling or exhaling while doing even simple movements may be frustrating. The teacher must respect this situation and tailor the directions to the student's capabilities.

After we see the student by teaching them one or two mild postures, we can identify whether this person is able to understand immediately whatever we say. Especially in *apanasana*, it is very difficult to make them understand to start with exhalation. Because most of the *asanas* start with inhalation. . . . So, observing the first few postures I am able to find out to what extent they can go. . . . Some housewives, in their 40s and 50s, after three classes only will I talk about breathing. To get into the movement itself they find difficult.

Focus and Simplicity in the Practice

Therapy courses for students at the KYM tend to be focused and brief, with fewer postures than were typically given several years ago. This trend may be due to students' increased time constraints, or to the need to give more class time to talking with the student, or simply a refinement in efficiency. In other words, nothing is superfluous in the practice. Every posture and technique is there for a purpose, and frequently, the simplest means are the most effective.

If you look at the course sheets [now], it will be fewer *asanas*. Before, [some years earlier] we used to give more—10 or 15, but now just four or three or sometimes two only. And sometimes only *pranayama*.

One teacher recalled the practice given him as a student when he first came to the KYM for help with asthma, and the contrast between this practice and his earlier experience in another yoga tradition.

Straight away [in the earlier classes] we started using *bhujangasana, salabasana, sarvangasana*—just a cluster of *asanas* arranged in some sequence. But after coming here

I found that simple *asana* like *dvipadapitham,* when I do with breathing, had much more effect on my system than all the other *asanas* put together.

This teacher reflected on comments made by his own students doing relatively simple postures. The effects are not easy to explain. "They feel a lightness in the body. They are able to move about better. They seem to have found their voice back. Their voice—they feel it is better."

Asked if the change in voice is related to the chanting the students are doing, the teacher replied,

Chanting, all of that. Especially the [students with asthma] say it. And some people say, "OK, I am not able to explain it, but I can definitely feel a difference." [And this is from] A simple, simple practice. Maybe it's a *bhavana* or something. We are not sure about how it really works because it is not investigated how it really works.

A teacher who is also a physician explained that simple movement with breathing can enhance the therapeutic effects of rest that is required in cases of acute back pain. Performing simple movements within the parameters of comfortable breathing provides a check on what movement is safe for the student.

Medical science says that for that type of acute problem [low back], rest to the particular area is most important. So we give the same thing. But added to that we give very simple, simple movements. Certain movements are resting for the back. But we take extra caution by [adding] breathing. We give the movement only within their breathing capacity so that it doesn't harm their system.

Using simple means rather than complex means in therapy does not suggest a limited knowledge of therapeutic interventions. To the contrary, using simple means requires knowledge. Depth of knowledge allows the teacher to select appropriate interventions and to be comfortable with simplicity.

In the ten years I have been associated with the Mandiram, one thing that has struck me is the simplicity. What we are teaching is very simple, very small techniques. But it does so many things. . . . Simple things come from all the knowledge. If we have the knowledge, then we can teach simple things. That is why we have anatomy and physiology, our Indian culture, all those things we have in the Diploma [training] program. Unless you have those things, the small things are not comfortable. If you have very little, then you teach in a superficial way.

In summary, tailoring the teaching to the individual student requires a holistic understanding of the student's situation. It precludes any falling back on a standard selection of *asanas* prescribed for a diagnosis separate from the entirety of the individual. Tailoring the practice to the particular student requires one-to-one interaction between teacher and student. This arrangement allows the teacher to gauge where to start and at what rate to progress. It supports the teacher's efforts to keep a clear focus in the student's practice, often employing the simplest of techniques. Tailoring the teaching to the individual, regardless of how simple are the means used, requires a solid and substantial basis for teaching. In the next chapter we examine the second theme derived from the interview data: Yoga practice aims at the mind while dealing with the body.

CHAPTER 3

AIMING AT THE MIND
WHILE DEALING WITH THE BODY

Atypical in the West where yoga is prized as a "workout," or as a good way to relieve stress, yoga in the tradition of T. Krishnamacharya pointedly maintains that "yoga is for the mind." *Patanjali's Yoga Sutra,* generally recognized as the definitive exposition on yoga, defines yoga as "the ability to control the thought waves of the mind" (Desikachar, 1987; Taimni, I. K., 1961). Yoga postures and breathing techniques serve to refine the entire system, but their ultimate aim is to make the mind a clear and accurate agent of perception (Desikachar, 1995).

Three constituent themes were identified in the interview data that generated the second major theme: Yoga practice aims at the mind while dealing with the body. Those themes are (a) Attending to and regulating the breath both in *asana* practice and in seated breathing practice focuses the activity of the mind, (b) Using sound in the practice, that is, chanting or vocalizing certain syllables, enhances both breathing and concentration, and (c) The student's mind-set when he embarks upon the practice greatly influences its success.

Using the Breath for Mental Focus

Probably all approaches to yoga acknowledge the close connection of the body, the breath, and the mind. In the tradition of T. Krishnamacharya as taught at the KYM, this connection is employed to the greatest possible advantage.

A teacher who had studied yoga in three other organizations before coming to the KYM was struck by the impact of breathing in *asanas*. "Here I was taught to inhale or exhale in all the movements. In the other places there was not much importance placed on the breathing." He was not immediately sold on the slower, simpler movements but "later on, I saw that this is really doing good."

All movement is based on the breathing, and consciously coordinating breath and movement both requires and cultivates mental focus.

> Although they are doing something mechanical, when they practice they are concentrating on [breathing]. . . . Combining breathing and movement in a systematic way, some feeling is there. That we see in all [students]. We do very simple movements. We give very simple breathing. But doing this for one day or one week, they feel some changes. They come out and say it. So it gives something not only for the body; it gives something for the mind also. That helps them.

Teachers frequently approach a physical problem by first giving breathing to calm the student's mind.

> I had a person who had asthma from childhood but mostly related to stress, and he had a lot of complicated problems, some back pain. I was thinking that his problem is related more to the mind because he would get something close to depression. He would say that if something happens at the office, he will get the asthma. So I thought that, more than the physical aspect of it, something relating to the mind, including breathing, had to be done. So I worked more in that direction. His asthma came down and he could face some of the situations.

Breathing practice is one of the tools to help students gain clarity about dilemmas in their lives. A teacher recalled a student during a lesson giving an emotional account of a problem she was experiencing in her personal life. Intuitively, the teacher decided to delay the seated breathing practice until after counseling her. The student was at first not able to consider the teacher's viewpoint. After her breathing practice, her mind was more clear. The mechanisms through which this clarity is gained are not easily explained.

> At first she did not like [what I said] at all. . . . So I said, "OK, now we will finish the last part and again we will talk." She finished her pranayama, and it was quite surprising. She

sat and she said, "What you say makes a lot of sense." I said, "You go home and do the practice again in the evening and then think about it." Next day, early morning, she called me and she said, "Thanks, thank you." So how can you explain these things, what therapy, what asanas, what do we do?

New students may not immediately appreciate the connection between breath and mind. The teacher may need to explain how breathing practices can help alleviate their problem.

[The case] was a man with anxiety when traveling alone. . . . For him, very simple *asanas*, all seated, arm movement, very simple. [At first] he closed his eyes and all that, and then, fourth *asana*, suddenly he said, "Madam, I don't think you have understood my problem. I don't see how sitting and breathing can help me." So I spoke to him about breathing. "It is very important here in Yoga Mandiram. . . . Like driving a car, the first thing is to learn the control of the steering. If you have that control, you can turn it, you can go anywhere you want. So like that you must have control of your breath." He was trying to understand. . . . And I said, "Yoga is a holistic science. We don't look at the physical aspect alone. It is both mental and physical." And I said, "What happens when you climb a flight of stairs vigorously?" He said, "Heavy breathing." I said, "When you walk in a very calm state of mind, what happens?" Then he started thinking: Breath plays a vital role; the breath is an indicator of the mind. He was very happy. He went home, and he practiced morning and evening.

Using Sound

When students have difficulty initiating exhalation in the abdomen or sustaining exhalation, the teacher may introduce sound. Production of sound in simple syllables or familiar chants necessitates abdominal control and facilitates a longer exhalation. A teacher described working with a young man who had many physical and psychological problems.

I found quite early that if he combined his exhale with a sound, a chant, even something simple like *Om shanti, shanti,* which he liked . . . . it was very effective for him. He could exhale for 10 or 12 seconds when he was saying *"Om shanti, shanti, shanti."* But if he didn't have a chant, if there was no sound there, his exhale would go right back to two seconds.

Many of the practices given to students, as evidenced in the documents on file at the KYM, include use of sound. This chanting may be done while seated or lying or while performing movement in the *asanas*. Using sound in *asana* is believed to aid in the student's concentration as well as making the posture more vigorous.

Creating the Mental Attitude

Teachers at the KYM believe that the student's mental attitude toward his practice is all important. That is why such effort is made in the first meetings with the student to help him relax and think positively about what he is about to begin. But the individual must want to do whatever needs to be done to improve his situation. A teacher still in the Diploma training program described her observations of two cases with similar diagnoses and the same teacher.

> This person had some hyperthyroid problem . . . . And she had lots of mental stress. But she has been coming here for the past six months. She is very regular with her practice. She feels that because of yoga her problems are solved. She has lost weight and is very happy. . . . The number of drugs she is taking has come down. And she takes all instructions very sincerely. We can see that she has benefited from the practice.

> That same day I [observed] another student with a similar problem. But this girl is 20, and she was brought by the mother. The moment the teacher said what she must do, she said, "I do not want to do that. Why should I do that?" No matter how much the teacher tried to convince this girl, she was very reluctant. She took it more as a challenge to prove herself than as something to help her. . . . She was supposed to come for the next class after a week, and she called, and the teacher asked, "Did you practice?" She said, "I did not practice." So same day, similar problem, but [different attitude].

If the practice does not engage the student mentally as well as physically, it will not work.

> Unless their mind really accepts it, they won't get the benefit of it. You can force a medicine on a person and it might work to quite an extent. But with yoga, it's different. . . . I have recommended [yoga] to quite a number of my friends because I have benefited so much. And [a friend] had a problem and she came here and she did this mechanically, and she said, "No, I didn't find it effective at all."

Sometimes the teachers use stories from ancient texts respected in India to help the student create a positive attitude toward their practice. A young woman experiencing severe agitation at the time of her menstrual periods demonstrated a negative attitude toward the course that was given to her. Her course included *surya namaskar* to make her more calm and *pranayama* to aid in her introspection.

She was quite skeptical about what was given to her. She said, "These *asanas* are going to help me? How do you think *pranayama* will help me? How do you think *surya namaskar* will help me?" So [the teacher] told her a story from one of our epics where Lord *Rama* goes across to an island to fight a demon. The demon had ten heads, and each time Lord *Rama* cut off one of his heads, the head would grow back. So he was not able to vanquish the demon. . . . So one of the *rishis* told him to do *surya namaskar.* "It will give you the mental focus and the concentration." So Lord *Rama* did *surya namaskar* and killed the demon. Oh, [the student] was very happy to hear that. She was asking questions . . . . I think it helped her to feel that this might help. So this sort of story is told just to motivate the student or make her feel positive. If she does not start the course with a positive attitude, it will not help her.

Just how the right frame of mind works in helping students succeed in their practice is not known. But the concept carries a great deal of weight with the teachers.

Whether it's the posture that helps, or the story, or what you build up around him—the *bhavana*—that helps—for me, most important is the mental impression he creates [even] before he starts doing this [practice]. What he thinks he will have out of this practice is more important than the practice itself. . . . To me, how we teach is more important than what we teach. I think [almost] anything will work as long as the person has the right mental framework.

In summary, assuming the primacy of the mind in the human system influences every aspect of teaching at the KYM. Consciously directing the breath in coordination with movement in *asanas*, the practice of *pranayama,* the use of sound, and building a particular attitude around the practice all serve to influence the mind in a positive way. The next chapter addresses the third major theme derived from interviews with the teachers at the KYM: The teachers feel a deep personal commitment to the lineage of T. Krishnamacharya.

CHAPTER 4

COMMITMENT TO THE
LINEAGE OF T. KRISHNAMACHARYA

P articipants in this study consistently indicated a strong personal commitment to the tradition upon which the Krishnamacharya Yoga Mandiram was founded. The constituent themes of this major theme are: (a) All teachers received, and continue to receive, systematic training in this approach to yoga, (b) Each has a teacher who works with him or her individually, and each maintains a regular, personal practice, (c) The teachers are engaged in on-going study of the *Yoga Sutra* and find meaningful application of this text in their own lives, (d) The teachers have a strong faith that supports them in this work, and (e) Their study and their work at the KYM are sources of personal development and gratification for them.

Training in the Tradition: the Diploma Program

The teachers came to the KYM by several different paths. Most, but not all, were students at the KYM before they embarked on teacher training. Of those who were students, most came seeking relief from a specific health problem. A few of the teachers were enticed into the training program by teachers already on the staff. Others simply responded to an announcement in the newspaper inviting applicants for the Diploma (teacher training) program. At least one of them was more attracted to the atmosphere at the KYM than to yoga itself.

> Honestly, when I joined [the Diploma program] I was really overwhelmed by the presence
> of the place — something that is in this atmosphere. I won't say that I was too much at-
> tracted to yoga at the beginning. What attracted me was the people here, how they behave,
> this whole culture of teacher and student relationship. It is different from what you see in
> the college; the care and concern that you learn is much more here. You get linked up to
> some source. My attachment to yoga came only later, after I started teaching.

In recent years, the Diploma program has attracted far more applicants than there are
spaces. Teachers most recently accepted into the Diploma program reported that only
15 seats were available in their Diploma class; over a hundred people applied. Applicants
are selected after an entrance exam and an interview. One informant speculated on the
selection process.

> Of course 50 percent taking the entrance exam probably get a 100 mark. It is not the
> major criterion. They are looking into how much you will give service to other people.
> And if you once join, can you come regularly? They will look into the circumstances, take
> everything into account.

The participants spoke enthusiastically about the content of their Diploma course.
They noted the distinctions between eastern and western approaches to therapy.

> It satisfied my curiosity in so many ways, like anatomy and physiology were very interesting.
> And *Yoga Sutra* gave us so many ideas which really I did not know before, so many hidden
> meanings. . . . And the *Ayurveda* class was what really opened my eyes to the different
> way in which western medicine operates and the [yoga] tradition operates. My faith [in
> the yoga tradition] became all the more strong. And other classes like preparation of an
> *asana* course, modification for therapy—I find that very interesting.

> We are learning the eastern and western schools of psychology. You see, western psy-
> chology stops with the mind, whereas the eastern school goes much beyond the mind.
> There is the *Atman,* for example, the *Purusa.* Western psychology stops with workings
> of the mind.

Content of the Diploma program is not static over time. It changes according to the
needs perceived by the teachers and faculty. Generally, the teacher-trainees experienced the
Diploma course as somewhat rigorous. The content was not limited to theory; application
was also required.

Normally in university studies, we will learn from the book. They will just ask questions and we will write it out. Here, it is not like that. If they explain one concept we will not just reproduce it in our exam paper. We will have to analyze and try to find out from that situation what concept it fits into. So it is not just mugging up and writing. It is more practical . . . . All papers are like that. Nothing is just reproduced.

We have three papers every semester. [For example], we had a paper on course planning where it was practical knowledge, like if you want to teach somebody this type of *pranayama*, or this type of *asana*, where do you start? What are the preparatory *asanas* you will teach them first to prepare the person to do this particular *asana?* So these were the type of questions asked in the practical papers where we had to demonstrate, teach somebody. And there would be three examiners watching us.

Each trainee in the Diploma program is given a "guide," a senior teacher who serves as their personal teacher and mentor. The guide also serves as the teacher-trainee's link to the "source." Explained by one teacher, "The main job of the guide is to see that you have a relationship that is beyond getting the diploma. The diploma is a means to get people linked up with yoga and with our teacher." The trainees observe their guides teaching individual students, and they write reports of their observations. Observing their guide is the primary way that teacher-trainees learn "how to give the instructions, how to talk to the student, how important it is to communicate."

The Diploma course runs for two years, with classes twice a week for the first three semesters. The final six months includes an internship. At this time, the trainees are given students to teach. Their first students generally are not therapy cases.

First they started giving me the younger ones with no serious problem, just to make them flexible or something to strengthen the back. And then slowly it's back pain and asthma. Now I am getting [students with] arthritis problems.

The consultant on duty and/or the trainee's guide are indispensable aids to the trainee's first efforts to teach. The consultant who first met with the student designs the first course. The trainee follows the consultant's direction.

So the first class I'll teach straight away. If I have any doubt, I'll call the consultant. Second class is mostly verification that they are doing the course correctly. Then from the third class I will take down the details of the back, what was his problem, is he feeling better, is there any difficulty in doing the *asanas,* is there any new problem, all those things, I'll write it down. Then I will go and call one of the consultants, whoever is there. I'll bring them inside. They will see the student. Then they will decide what more to teach. "OK, you remove this, you remove this, you add this." All those things I am given. Then I will give the class according to that requirement. After that I will draw the [stick figures illustrating the postures] and give it to him.

Even after the new teacher has completed the Diploma course, he continues to work under the guidance of the consultant. Having the most experienced and trained teachers overseeing the work of the newer teachers provides ongoing quality assurance. Asked how long the period lasts in which the consultant gives him direction on what to teach, a young teacher replied:

You cannot have a break there. One cannot take it up just like that. You see, here, the important thing is the therapeutic value. . . . The Mandiram is taking care so that whoever comes here should be given the maximum benefit. That's why we always have the guidance of our teachers to prepare the next course. It's not that we can't think on our own, but to benefit the student, we are advised. In turn, we ask whatever we want to ask, and so it gets clarified.

The teachers have access to their guide or a consultant whenever a problem occurs, even if it means interrupting that teacher's own class.

In the Mandiram, we never have a closed door policy: "Don't disturb; I am busy." We never do that. Even if my teacher is in class, I can say, "I've got this problem; please help me." The teacher will say, "OK, fine," even if he has a student there. . . . So in our training we know that we always have this. I think that is the greatest learning that we have. Whenever we have trouble, we have access to the teacher.

Experienced teachers also have a teacher to consult when they are unclear about what steps to take with a student. Many times they ask Desikachar to see a particularly complicated case. Or, "when everything is okay but there is no progress and I need to know how to take the person somewhere, then I go to him."

The development of new teachers is a process that takes time. But the more the new teacher becomes invested in learning, the more the Mandiram provides for that learning.

You cannot say all teachers are the same level. . . . We have beginners who are still not exposed to a lot of things. Perhaps they are just out of the Diploma course. . . . How much more time [they want to give] and how much more learning they want to do comes from them. And the minute that step is taken, the minute they show interest, we give them a lot more responsibility. And when they are able to take that responsibility, they get closer to what the other teachers are teaching. . . . So they watch us and see how we teach, how we do a consultation, or how to handle a particular person. That's how they learn . . . . slowly, with years of experience here. I don't think it just comes.

In this consultant's view, the senior teachers at the KYM are open and generous in their role as guides to the newer teachers. Their experience with their own teachers is what has influenced this attitude.

The teachers are the prime factors [in shaping new teachers] . . . . Not all teachers [everywhere] are so open to give and tell their students what they know. I think all of us here are fortunate to have teachers like Krishnamacharya and Desikachar to expose you to what they know. There is no hiding back, no keeping something to themselves.

The modeling done by the teachers' mentors includes the behavior that is so basic to the tradition of T. Krishnamacharya. That is, the teacher must treat each student as an individual.

We see Desikachar when he is doing the consultation. We observe how he deals with people, how he talks to a person. I think all that has an influence on the teacher. We cannot be the teachers we are without seeing the teachers in front of us. . . . If we saw a teacher just saying, "Oh, you have a headache. OK, let me take your pulse. Can you do this posture for me? I have seen this problem before, so this is what you have to do. This is your practice." If we saw our teachers doing that, that is what we would be doing. But that's not what Desikachar is; that's not what Krishnamacharya was. . . . We learn everything from this heritage.

Teacher's Personal Practice

The teacher's personal practice "helps us sustain this heritage." It is a given that each teacher at the KYM maintains a consistent, personal yoga practice. The informants were not asked if they practice regularly, but several referred to the importance of their personal practice.

> [My practice] is part of my life. . . . You have to feel comfortable with yourself doing it. Only then can you expect others to do it. . . . If somebody asked me, "What do you think is the most important thing that you do as a teacher?" I think [personal practice] would be the most important. We expect every [teacher] to do regularly.

Their own practice and its influence on their daily lives is the foundation for their role as teachers.

> You know, what we are learning through books and all these classes is actually very little. Here is the real learning: We are taught how to live yoga and not how to speak it. We don't say something and do something else. All our teachers practice yoga so we believe in yoga.

The teacher's yoga practice, like any other individual's practice in the tradition of T. Krishnamacharya, addresses the mind as much as the body. The teachers recognize that their practice helps them keep the mind fresh and a most useful tool.

> Man has a mind that, whatever it does, is able to do successfully. If you give it anything, it can do it. That's the mind. So this yoga helps your mind to be like that. If you keep it fresh, it is all the time ready to receive, ready to give. Unless it receives, it cannot give. And there is no end to learning.

The practice also creates a mental space that allows the teacher to reflect and draw from deeper sources of understanding. In a discussion of the need for a teacher to be clear on the boundaries of her role as a therapist, this informant associated her process of maintaining clarity with her practice of reflection or meditation.

> We call it reflection—meditation if you want to put it sophisticated. You have to meditate. Meditation tells you where you stand, what is your purpose in life. Once you get that, you know where you stand.

Another teacher with a demanding profession in addition to teaching yoga described how his morning practice helps prepare his body and mind for his day's work. After work, he does a practice to help him make the transition to his teaching at the KYM.

So I go home and I take some 5 minutes or 10 minutes for my practice so again I can do something else. A very simple practice between my work and this so that I can be a little more effective. . . . [The practice] prepares you for your life.

Studying the *Yoga Sutra*

All the teachers study the *Yoga Sutra* in their training program as well as in lectures offered regularly at the KYM. The lectures illustrate how the *sutras* apply to ordinary life.

After a consistent year of listening to [Desikachar's] *Yoga Sutra* class, I am constantly amazed. . . . He will start talking about how he was irritated with his wife this morning because she was cooking beans, and he doesn't like beans, . . . And as he relates this, he is talking about the *Sutra*. In the beginning [I may have] no idea what he is talking about but he brings it around to say, "here is an everyday example."

Seeing the practicality of the *sutras* has a big impact on the teacher's personal development. One of them expressed that the *Yoga Sutra* "opened my eyes, because I was able to understand things, how to look at things, and how to change myself."

Their own grounding in the *Yoga Sutra* gives the teachers a basis for counseling their students and helping them find solutions to their problems.

We don't tell them directly that "these are the *sutras* that are applicable to you." That becomes theory. . . . But putting it into practice for my own self and implementing that in my own life, that is different [from theory]. . . . I just keep a lot of notes with me and then forget about it. But we definitely apply those *sutras* to help students come out of certain problems.

[The *Yoga Sutra*] is a great book on psychology. . . . I am able to relate every case to one of the *sutras*—why it happens, what is the cause. . . . I don't use the words, *"Yoga Sutra"* [with the students], but I talk to them with that great text in my mind.

Faith and Commitment to the Lineage

Faith in their teachers and faith in the process of which they are a part provide tremendous support for the teachers at the KYM. They spoke of "faith in a force that is working to guide me."

I can face any situation because the confidence is there that I can do what best I can do and beyond that, I'll forget it. Krishnamacharya said that if the human being has lost all his qualities except one—faith, that will make up for it. I have the confidence that something will take care of it, in spite of obstacles.

The connection that the teachers feel between themselves and the lineage that the KYM represents gives them confidence, as expressed in, "We call upon the blessings of the guru. We take it to that level." Feeling that they are representing that lineage when they teach makes them want to give their best. "You see, we have more responsibility because we are representing a great teaching. So every case that comes, I feel it is not just me teaching. It's the great thing behind us." Another teacher confirmed this position.

One thing we always have in mind whenever we handle a student is that it's not the [individual] teacher who is handling the student. [The students] are not going to refer to that teacher outside. They are going to say, "Krishnamacharya Yoga Mandiram." They say, "I went to KYM, I got this, or I didn't get this." So I feel that as part of this place, we should give our best. Because it's not my name; it's the Mandiram's name.

If a student at the KYM wants to change teachers, the teacher is not offended. "We are here because of the student. The student is not here because of us." Commitment to the KYM rather than to themselves as individual teachers helps them keep their ego in check.

Nowadays there is not much ego problem [among teachers at the KYM]. Because we believe we are working for the Mandiram. And we have to do good for the people. So our focus is on the students. If we show our ego, then what happens to the students?

Teachers' commitment to the lineage that the KYM represents is deep and rewarding. This commitment is based on what the teachers have experienced themselves, as expressed by one teacher, " Whatever I can contribute to the Mandiram, I do it wholeheartedly. . . . It is difficult to explain that sort of personal feeling that you have for a place. Maybe it is because it has changed me so much."

Personal Development/Intrinsic Rewards

Almost all the teachers described the intrinsic rewards they experience through helping other people. The deep satisfaction from helping people alleviate problems evolves over time with their own practice, study and experience.

> Actually when I started learning, I was not doing it as a social service. That was not the idea. . . . Yoga had done me a lot of good and that was the reason I [began training to teach]. . . . I was not even aware of the therapeutic side of yoga. I never knew that yoga would help back pain, cervical pain.

> Today after so much experience I find that I am happy if somebody comes back and tells me, "I am fine; I am doing better." That is something that cannot be explained so easily. . . . I wouldn't say that it is an ego bloating. I am very aware that yoga is a technique, and the technique is what [is doing it]. I am not personally doing a lot in that. I am giving him some process, a process that he does [himself]. So there is a satisfaction that I did not have in my earlier job situation.

This teacher spoke of his own "evolution," that "something is taking place in me." He attributed that evolution partly to "a lot of oppurtunities to look at oneself." Others related their personal development to a new perspective on their own problems that resulted from their work at the KYM.

> For me it has been a terrific internal development. . . . It is how I have learned to look at the world, being in this institute. I have learned a lot. I have learned to see people. I have learned to see that what I have in my life is no misery compared to so many people who come with problems. So I know how much more positive I have to be in my own life, to be grateful to my teachers, to the Lord above me who has kept me here.

One teacher spoke of her own *dharma* requiring her to do this work. Believing that she is fulfilling her *dharma* is a source of satisfaction for her.

Yoga is something that comes from my soul. My [other] job is for my ego and for my mind. My family is for my *karma,* but my soul is in yoga. . . . There [have been] many times it would have been easy for me to withdraw from [teaching] and not get into anything. But this is something I have to do because it is my duty; it is my *dharma.* . . . It comes from deep within me, so I have to do it. . . . But I feel that I have evolved into a better person because of yoga. That makes me feel happy that I am in this life.

In summary, teachers at the KYM are supported by the guidance they receive from their own teachers, and they see themselves as representatives of this lineage. The connection they feel with the KYM bolsters their faith in something higher than themselves. Their commitment is further supported by their own study and practice, and by the personal gratification they receive from teaching. The next chapter examines the fourth major theme in this study of yoga therapy at the KYM: The teacher-student relationship substantially supports the healing process.

CHAPTER 5

HEALING THROUGH RELATIONSHIP

W hen the teacher and student work one-to-one over a period of time, the connection between the two individuals becomes a force in the healing equation. A teacher expressed, "It's not just moving an arm or a hand because there is so much inter-relationship between the student and the teacher for that one hour in the class. And that brings a lot of personal development within the student." Desikachar (1998) speaks of the relationship between a yoga teacher and student as an "absolute bond of trust that must exist . . ." (p. 186) and that "is essential to the progress of an individual in yoga." (p. 182). This particular perspective on the relationship between teacher and student is shaped by Krishnamacharya's fundamental admonition that the teacher must have "absolute respect for the individual, absolute devotion to the infinite potential within each of us" (p. 181). Most of the informants in this study were not asked directly what they believe constitutes the healing relationship. But several aspects of this relationship emerged in their interviews. Components of this theme are: (a) the student's faith, (b) the teacher's attitudes toward the student, (c) empathic listening, and (d) fostering independence.

The Student's Faith

In many cases, when students decide to come to the KYM, they have already begun to adopt an attitude of faith and hope.

When people come here, either they have tried many other systems and it has not worked, and they [decide to] give this a try, or somebody says, "Go to yoga; it will help you." So they come with a hope. They have this faith that something good will happen here. Most people come here because somebody has recommended it. So [working with them] is easier than if it is without faith.

The student's faith in the process is bolstered as he sees the care with which the KYM staff deals with his problem.

Here, at least three people see the student—the consultant, the teacher, the supervisor. Sometimes there may be more than one supervisor. Sometimes [Desikachar] comes into the room. So at least three, minimum. So the student feels like he is very precious. It is important. You ask what develops that faith. This is what develops the faith—being treated so well.

The teacher's accessibility to the student also contributes to a trusting relationship. Many of the teachers let the students know that they may call them at home if needed.

We have mutual respect. They know that as a teacher I am looking at their needs as most important. They have access to me. They can telephone me, contact me when they want. I don't say, "You can call only during this time." They can call whenever they want. A few days ago one of our teachers got a call at nearly midnight. Sometimes 4:00 o'clock in the morning. They know they have a shoulder to lean on. That causes a good relationship because they have a confidence in the teacher. That confidence in the teacher helps this relationship.

The teachers who revealed their policy of giving students their home phone numbers believe that maintaining a supportive link with the student is important. They did not experience this as a problem. Said one teacher, "They know my timing. They know we go to bed very early. So if they call, they call before 9:00 o'clock. They don't disturb me at all." Similarly, another teacher expressed how she handled the situation and why it is important.

It is not that I give my telephone number to everyone. But [I do to] some people whom I feel that they need contact; just by talking they feel a little better. Then if those people do call up at odd times, sometimes we tell them, "It is not convenient to talk; can you call at a different time?" That is okay. . . . That link is what we are trying to protect.

Students working with a teacher at the KYM gradually gain confidence. The effect of their own practice builds this confidence in themselves as well as in their teacher.

> Their confidence in us is the reason they do whatever we ask them to do. And of course, their practice goes on side by side. You see, they have confidence in what they are practicing. That is why all these things are happening. The students get a lot of confidence from their practice. That is what is making them [confide in us] also. . . . Just after two classes, three classes, you don't become [that] close to each other. It's just half an hour, 45 minutes. It's their personal practice. If they do the practice regularly and sincerely, I'm sure they will have this sort of feeling that they have.

Even short, simple practices, which the student associates with the lineage at the KYM, can be the vehicle for building the student's confidence.

> I have a student, [an elderly man] who says, "You are my *guru* so I think of Krishnamacharya, I think of Desikachar, I think of you, and then only do I start my practice." And what have I given to him? It's only arm movements, side and front, and then *sitali pranayama.*

The regard and affection that students develop for their teachers may seem a major influence on their maintaining a practice and continuing classes at the KYM. But the student's attraction to the teacher's personality is not enough. Only what the student experiences himself will sustain the practice over time.

> As a yoga teacher, certainly I would be very happy to influence a person to [practice]. But I think it is beyond that. . . . Because we are giving a technique to him. That technique is given in an individualized course, and sometimes our personality might influence him, but that is only to some extent. I think it is only to attract an individual. Beyond that, what "stuff" is there is very important. That stuff is practice. . . . If it is me that is [causing him to come], the person may come back to me often but he may not even practice. That means yoga is not there. I think that will not work for long.

When "yoga is not there," that is, the student does not practice or does not return for continuing lessons, how do teachers view this situation? A relatively new teacher expressed his feeling that it is his fault when students do not return after the first or second class, that he has "not gained their confidence." A teacher with more experience looked at the situation differently.

Some cases just don't work out. . . . We accept it. I don't [consider cases] a personal success or a personal failure. . . . I do have students who don't come back after the first class. It's just that they are not ready. I always go through the course and [think about] where I might have slipped, or have not talked to them well. But I don't worry about it. It is an education for us. . . . Maybe they are not able to practice, so they don't want to come. Maybe someone at home does not want them to come. . . . It could be any number of reasons. So why feel bad about it? You have given your best.

The Teacher's Attitude toward the Student

The trust with which students come to the KYM increases the teachers' sense of responsibility to the students.

In India, doctors send people here. . . . And doctors can say, "This is a problem case; there is no cure for it. We wash our hands of it." We can't say that. We have more responsibility because people come here with trust. . . . We can't say, "No, you can't come here; we don't have an answer for you." At least we must try. The least we can do is give hope. We cannot say, "I will cure you." We can only say, "I will try to help you."

Teachers whose association with the KYM began as students themselves were introduced early to a particular attitude that the tradition of T. Krishnamacharya fosters in teachers. That attitude is that "the student is most important."

The teachers here know how they have been treated [as students]. They know that they were the most important when they were sitting on the side as students. We are trained like this. We have been given this teaching right from the days of [Krishnamacharya].

In quiet, inconspicuous ways, teachers "go the extra mile" giving personal attention to their students. This generosity of spirit has been modeled for them by their own teachers.

What I received here was a lot of personal attention from my teacher. I remember her asking me to apply something on my skin [for a rash]. She had gone to a temple to get it [for me]—that sort of thing. And I see [teachers] doing it. It's not asking somebody to go and get it; they take the car and go get it. So I try to give as much personal attention as I can to students. It's like what you get, you give. So that keeps it going. I think it has helped me to become a better teacher.

Some teachers with years of experience described changes in their views and attitudes toward teaching. Whereas earlier they regarded the technical aspects of teaching as most important, they now feel that their manner with the student carries more weight than their technical expertise.

Slowly I have changed, you see. [Now] I talk to them very freely. And I take so much interest. Before I didn't know this idea—that you have to show compassion. [Earlier] I thought being a teacher means that you have to be [a certain way]. I didn't know the relationship should be good like this. So, slowly I have understood that it is the relationship that works, more than the *asanas*.

They see their teaching as "not just giving an *asana* practice." They see the importance of having a personal interest in the student also.

Initially, when I started teaching, I just taught some postures. . . . If you are raising the arms, it should be on inhalation. If you are lowering your arms, it should be on exhalation. How is the breathing pattern? Are you breathing from chest or from stomach, you know? These are the things I observed initially. But I have decided there should be [a certain] quality in my teaching. It is not just somebody coming, taking some postures, just teaching and sending them off. . . . So [now] I take a personal interest in each case. I find out what is the problem before going to the class. At the end of the day, I sit and think about the case. . . . So you go deep into the personal aspect and discuss [with them] their problems. So some sort of personal touch I have developed with each of my students.

Teachers' attitudes that contribute to the healing relationship may be astonishingly simple, based on genuine concern for the student.

When you are in the teacher's chair and you do this yoga therapy for students, you pray for them. I think of my students every day, and though I don't remember their names, I remember faces. So I generally pray for them and I wish them good luck. That's all. Nothing more than that.

Even with the teacher's best intentions, some students may fail to practice on their own as regularly as is needed. Or they may stop practicing altogether. What is the teacher's

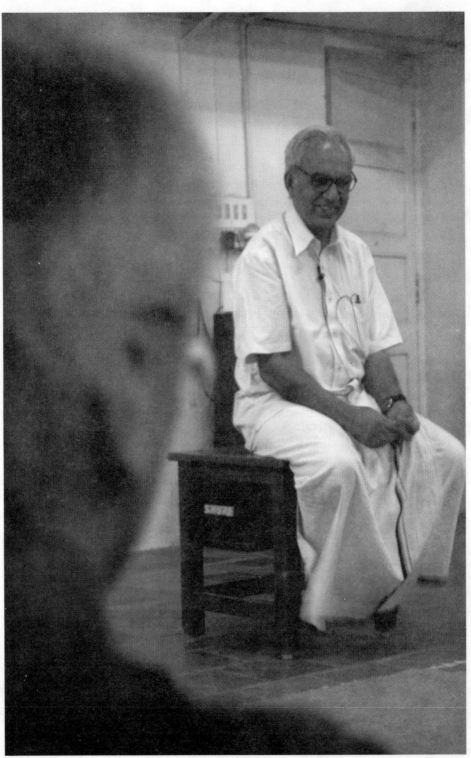

attitude toward this student? Personal maturity and respecting the tradition shape this informant's response.

> We never tell the student, "you are not doing it regularly, so don't come back." I think the student has the freedom to say, "I don't want this teacher," or "I don't want to do this yoga." That's fine. But as teachers who are passing on a tradition of teaching, I think it is important for us to accept them as they are today. Maybe students who don't practice, maybe they do once a week, twice a week, and they come, but we keep seeing them. Not seeing them is not a solution. . . . We talk to them, try to find out why they are not able to do, maybe it is not effective, maybe I can change the teacher, I can [consult with somebody] . . . . But there are so many things we can try that I think, never should we [dissolve the relationship] once they come. Because that is this teaching. It is what has been given to us—a divine gift or something which should help. . . . This is not something that you can understand right at the beginning of your teaching career. One grows into that.

Empathic Listening

Teachers learn that being with a student requires a particular frame of mind, that is, being fully attentive to the person. "Unless you have that attitude of being with the person totally, you will not be able to [help] him." This focused attention enables the teacher to listen carefully and empathetically. The student's talking itself is therapeutic.

> They are longing for [someone] to hear their problems, to bring out whatever they are feeling. You see, when still it is there [inside you], it will keep on giving you trouble. Once it comes out you will feel relaxed.

Psychological problems presented by the student may be greater than the physical problems. Allowing the student to talk and listening empathetically may be a better use of class time than giving *asanas.*

> Today we are facing situations where their medical condition is fine. Blood pressure, heartbeat, pulse, everything is fine. But something else is happening which is causing a depression. . . . One of the main things nowadays is that people can't speak to anybody. Sometimes their problem becomes like a taboo for them. So they are controlling their

emotions. So what I ask them to do is speak. I listen. So it pours from them. They just pour out sometimes. They talk and talk and then they feel better.

I have a student about 22 years old, very, very thin. She does not have a good appetite. She would always get a pain, back, hand, everything. So I would struggle with her like everything. [Consultant] would help me for her. Every week I would change her course. When I give her something to take care of the hand, next time she will say, "I get [the pain] here." . . . All over the body she will say, "this pain is here, that pain is there." . . . So we talk with them a lot. For some students I spend two classes just talking and listening. Then only will I give the class.

A teacher with many years experience uses self-disclosure when she believes it would help her student. Asked how she creates a good relationship with students, her reply reinforces the "generosity of spirit" noted earlier in this discussion.

I just act naturally. I don't keep anything inside. I want to teach them what all I know. I listen to their problem, and then if I know something, I give them some solutions from my personal experience. They like that because they are human beings also. They can understand. So when they have some problems, I prod them and then I talk with them, and then slowly they will tell everything, and we become so close.

This particular teacher's skill as a listener/counselor was described by a younger teacher who had observed many of her classes.

She works very fast; she is sort of concise and direct. Yet she has a quality about her. . . . Maybe it's the way she looks; maybe it's the way she listens, but she has a certain quality where people just open up to her. She doesn't question a lot and she doesn't impose—she just creates a space where people will reveal information to her. She is very human yet she doesn't get bogged down in [the person's tragedy]. . . . She's empathic, but she doesn't lose herself in it, and she has a firm grounding to relate it to. . . . Whereas I've observed other classes where teachers make themselves very open and available, but the same link, the same created space—whatever you want to call it—isn't there.

The skills used by the teacher described above are not necessarily what would be taught in a formal course in counseling. They may even violate some of the traditional guidelines followed by professional counselors. Experienced teachers appear to pull from their own grounding in yoga, coming from years of study and practice. One teacher described this as attempting to transmit a sense of clarity to her students.

You speak of "counseling skills," such as not advising, having eye contact, not giving interpretation—so those are counseling skills. But in yoga it is different from this. [A few minutes ago] when I was talking with the person in that room, that person was under stress. He can't even sit. I just listened. And when I listen I am trying to put myself in that person's position. And the thing is, he expects that by coming and seeing me he will get some solutions to his problem. . . . So this type of counseling is very different. We try to help him analyze and see the situation. . . . It could be called interpretation or it could be taken as giving clarity . . . . but I don't call it counseling.

It is the way you live your life, and you try to transmit a certain part of your life to that person—clarity of thinking, a sense of balance, not to be worked up about a situation, trying to be a little more stable, that's all. So to do that, we use certain concepts . . . . [such as] to be able to accept the consequences of what we do. . . . This is our philosophy, to take things as they come. But I can't say that to him; he will say, "That lady is talking philosophy to me." But from my point of view, I am trying to make the person understand that we are not the controller of everything in our lives. . . . When you have that clarity in your [own] mind, you tend to give [the student] a sense of clarity.

The teacher's grounding and sense of clarity help give the student courage to face their problems. As expressed by one, "I don't cry with them or anything like that. They feel good to talk to me because they want somebody who is bold. They say that."

No teacher expressed that listening to students' personal problems was burdensome to them. But the interviewer suggested that possibility. An experienced teacher described how she avoids becoming weighted down with what students share with her; she does not carry it with her. She also has faith that things will work out for the student "because that's how it was for me."

Whatever students say, I listen to them, and I try to talk to them and help them out then and there. And then the next person comes and I don't even remember what the first person told me until I see her the next time. . . . I am very compassionate with them. I talk to them with a lot of love and care and I listen to them carefully. But at the same time, I have a confidence that they have come here, and that is going to take care of them, and everything is going to be alright. So I shift my attention to the next person so that I am not with them anymore.

Even when she teaches several members of the same family and knows intimate details of their relationships, she respects each of them as individuals. Maintaining confidentiality helps secure the student-teacher relationship.

The mother, the daughter, her sister, and her sister's husband—all are coming to me. So if I even utter one word, there will be a big gossip in the family. So I just forget about this girl when I see her brother-in-law. I don't even see him as her brother-in-law. All that is not in my mind. I see him as he is. I don't even tell him, "She came for her class," or "He came for his class." I totally avoid. It's not that I am being careful, but I never talk about one student to another student, even if it's husband and wife. So they have confidence that nothing goes out of here. What we talk with them about, nobody else knows. . . . So [students] have a lot of confidence. That is why sometimes they do whatever we ask them to do.

Fostering Independence

Teachers at the KYM not only attempt to help the student reduce the problem for which they have come, but also to strengthen the individual so that the problem will not return. Part of the effort to strengthen the individual is to foster independence in his practice, rather than dependence on the teacher.

I have a student whom I have been seeing for some time. He brought his grandson here and said, "Please give him some practice. Please see him every day." He wants me to see him every day because that grandson will practice in front of my eyes. But I see him [only] once a week. I said, "You have to have the responsibility. Practice at home." He said, "When can I practice? I have to go to school; I have to—." I said, "Practice whenever you want. Don't wait for Saturday and Sunday. Practice every day whenever you want. But once a day you practice." He's a young boy; it is not going to matter how long since he finished eating. So we are giving them independence.

Even young children are taught without the parent's presence.

Unless the child has mental retardation, we don't want the parent to come in. I had a problem once with a mother who came. She had two sons who were students. And she wanted to attend the classes. She said, "I want to see so that I can correct them in the house." I said, "You don't have to do it. Please give them the responsibility." I explained to her. She had some problems with it, but later she understood. She didn't even come to the Mandiram with them; they came with a driver and car. . . . . So they have to do it on their own. If I am dependent on somebody and that person is absent, I am finished. But they have to be educated. There are so many people who want to become dependent.

Other more subtle ways of interacting with the student help build his ability to rely on himself. One of them is to avoid manually adjusting the student's posture.

Our teaching is to help people depend on themselves. For example, we don't touch people when we teach them. If someone is keeping his leg like this, not like this, we ask them, "Put your leg like this." We don't turn it. Because once I turn it, he expects me to turn it next time. Nobody's going to turn it [at home]. The teaching is not going through his head. So we say, "Turn your leg." So he, on his own, will turn his leg.

Students seeing more than one teacher at the KYM also helps avoid dependency and attachment to a particular teacher.

It also helps that three people are seeing them. So they don't get attached to the person. "Ah, this man saw me; only he will teach me. Only this lady saw me; only she can teach me." No, first the consultant, then this person, then a supervisor. So they get comfort- able changing teachers. They don't get attached. We teach in different rooms. There is a freedom. We don't say, "always this room." In any room available, we teach.

Helping the student find resources within himself, rather than advising him on everything he should do or should not do, fosters independence.

When people come here, they are coming with a disturbed mind. Now if you start off by being too advisory, it is not going to help. They have already had a lot of advice. So [the practice] must give that person confidence that he has the resources himself. He doesn't have to look outside for the resources. That needs to be seen, depending on the individual. . . . I've found that new teachers do a lot of advising. They will learn. Advice is an external resource.

We normally don't tell them what not to do. We will only advise them, "If you do that it will not be helpful." So it should be on the part of the student to observe and analyze that it [the behavior] will not do anything for them. Based on that, they can make a better decision.

At least one teacher acknowledged the fine line that exists between the student's independence and dependency, particularly when the relationship is very close.

It is definitely a problem. But what is yoga? Yoga is to make independent. Though they sometimes depend on us—sometimes they may call us—but they are not completely dependent on us. We are very close; at the same time, we are a little away also. . . . But when we talk with them, we tell them,—"You have to take care of yourself; you have to stand on your own feet."

Teachers understand that their relationship with students is not the same as being "friends." They must "be able to leave it at the end of the day." One of them described how she attempts to maintain that distance even while her behavior shows a lot of caring.

I try to keep that little bit of distance. . . . I don't talk about myself. Not much. I mean just enough to make them comfortable. . . . [When you don't talk about] your personal emotions, I think it is easier to keep a distance, so that they see us only as a teacher. We try not to have any other contact with them, socially, or otherwise. Only here, in the Mandiram, not in the house or anywhere else.

But the teacher/student relationship demands that the teacher be ever alert to its dynamics. Ego, dependency, attachment—all are fodder for the teacher's reflection on her role as a teacher and a practitioner of yoga.

A part of you gets elation when somebody gets relieved of their problem. Initially I had a sense of "I have done something" and all that. . . . But you can't succeed in all cases. You can't be the god who does everything. So what happens, you get that happiness [with success] and you tend to forget where the limit is, and you tend to create unnecessary hope in the people, and you are starting a chain of dependency. And that dependency itself you foster and foster. But yoga is not dependence. Yoga is complete freedom and independence, both for the student and for the teacher. So I realized as I was teaching that this is not right; it is a pitfall.

Everybody wants to be taken care of. And we love to take care of people. But you try to balance . . . . This clarity comes to a yoga teacher once she realizes what is possible for her and what is not possible for her. *Satya* and *asatya*. What is right and what is wrong. And that we are only an instrument in the process. We are not saviors of the world.

In summary, the relationship between student and teacher appears to be a significant aspect of the healing process. As revealed in conversations with these teachers, the healing relationship is characterized by the student's trust and faith in the teacher and in the process, the teacher's attitude that the student is most important, the teacher's ability and willingness to listen, and the independence that is fostered in the student. Chapter six gives a summary of the four major themes derived from the interviews, the limitations of the study, and supporting evidence of these findings, based on the researchers' observations of actual classes.

CHAPTER 6

This naturalistic study identifies and provides insight into processes involved in yoga therapy at the Krishnamacharya Yoga Mandiram in Chennai, India. This chapter summarizes the findings and discusses the limitations of the study. The findings from the interview data are then examined in light of supporting evidence.

Summary

The fundamental premise of yoga therapy at the KYM is that the unique characteristics of the individual student determine the yoga practices given to the student. Teachers at the KYM use no standard set of practices to treat the problem for which help is sought. Two students with the same clinical diagnosis, for example, asthma, are unlikely to receive identical courses. These individuals will differ in other health issues, physical structure, age, occupation, etc. The yoga practice developed for each of them takes these and other factors into account.

The initial consultation with the new student gives the consultant the first opportunity to ascertain the nature and scope of the student's problems. The consultant's observation and the student's verbal input are the chief sources of information. The consultant also uses this first session to help the student develop a positive attitude toward his prognosis and the yoga practice that he will soon begin. The consultant determines the initial focus of the practice, designs the first course, and chooses a teacher for this particular student.

All yoga therapy classes are taught one-to-one. Consultants continue to guide the teacher, overseeing the student's progress and subsequent changes in the practice. Meantime, the teacher develops a rapport with the student and supports the student's confidence that his practice will have positive results. Over time, the teacher learns more about the student's greater life situation. The web of factors that influence the student's well-being becomes more clear, and the teacher is able to address areas other than the problem originally identified by the student.

Early in the classes, the teacher discovers the appropriate level at which to introduce the various elements in the practice, recognizing that this, too, cannot be standardized. The complexity and amount of verbal instruction given while teaching the course also varies among individual students. The teacher must be particularly attentive, intuitive, knowledge-able, and patient. Subsequent practices respond to the student's progress, other problems that may emerge, and the changing circumstances in the student's life.

Therapy courses are efficient in their focus and length. Taking into account multiple factors, the practices are often quite brief. Simple movements and breathing with appropriate permutations are found to be remarkably effective. But simplicity in the practices does not imply limited resources. To the contrary, using simple means to achieve the desired end requires a refined level of understanding of the means and ends of yoga.

The various movements given in the student's course are all based on conscious, regulated breathing. The student learns how and with what movements to inhale or exhale, and to regulate the length and quality of the breath. By necessity, this integration of breath and movement focuses the mind and serves to sustain that focus throughout the practice. Practices generally end with a few minutes of seated or lying breathing, further contributing to a quiet, clearer state of mind.

Students may be taught to use vocal sound in movement and/or during the breath-ing practice following the postures. The production of sound strengthens the breath and improves concentration. Chanting that is appropriate for the individual's religious orientation may also reinforce his spiritual awareness. Both the regulation of breath and the use of sound are intended to engage the student's mind in a focused, increasingly refined way.

Practices are ultimately aimed at the mind, based on the principle that healing involves the mind as much or more than the body.

Teachers at the KYM undergo a structured, two-year Diploma program including a six-months internship under an experienced teacher. But their training is ongoing through continuing classes, lectures, and staff meetings. Perhaps more important to their education is their continuing work with their guide (personal teacher) and their easy access to the consultants (senior teachers). New teachers meet with their mentors regularly, and mentors frequently drop in on the teachers' classes.

The teachers maintain their own mental and physical well-being through a personal, disciplined yoga practice which they consider an essential foundation for teaching. Studying the *Yoga Sutra* while integrating those teachings into their daily lives helps the teachers understand themselves and others, and enables them to impart some sense of clarity to their students seeking solutions to problems.

Underlying the work that teachers do at the KYM is a deeply felt connection and commitment to the lineage of T. Krishnamacharya. Representing the lineage rather than themselves as individual teachers motivates them to give their best, without ego-centered-ness. In the process, they gain a great deal of inner satisfaction and personal development. They have learned to see themselves and others better through their teaching. They spoke of "personal evolution" and fulfilling a duty that comes from deep within.

The relationship that develops between teacher and student is paramount to the healing that occurs in yoga therapy. The relationship is based on mutual respect, the faith and trust that the student has in the teacher and in the lineage, and the self-confidence the student gains through his developing practice. Teachers learn early on that the tradition they represent is fundamentally "student-centered." They take personal interest in their students and treat them with care and generosity of spirit. They encourage and allow their students to talk about their concerns, listening with empathy and support.

While giving support, the teachers deliberately attempt to foster their students' independence. They help the students think for themselves in their yoga practice as well as in their life situations. They adroitly show caring while avoiding emotional attachment between the two of them. Finding this balance is a skill that comes from the teacher's own personal development. Keys to the teacher's ability to create this relationship appear to be: insight into herself and her role as a teacher, mental clarity, and acceptance that "we are only instruments in the process; we are not saviors of the world."

Limitations of the Study

This study has a number of limitations. One is that the processes of yoga therapy were examined only from the teachers' perspectives. The "other side of the coin," and certainly essential to an accurate picture of these processes, is the perspective of students. Interviews with students at the KYM and members of their families would yield invaluable data in this effort to grasp the dynamics of yoga therapy. Future studies seeking to understand the experience and perspectives of students receiving yoga therapy are warranted.

It would be beneficial in future studies if the interviewers were natives of the culture. In this study, the American interviewer and the Indian teachers encountered some difficulty in understanding each other's English and idioms. The difficulty was not significant, however, and was lessened by the teachers' generous spirit of cooperation with the project.

Another limitation was the lack of opportunity for the interviewer to conduct follow-up interviews. Additional clarification on some issues and confirmation of the researcher's conclusions would be valuable. But the researcher's limited time on site and distance from the site precluded this "member-checking" of conclusions that is expected in qualitative research. However, observations by the other two members of the research team were done over a greater period of time and were comprehensive enough to add considerable support to the findings of the study. This supportive evidence is presented in the section below.

Finally, the unique circumstances at the Krishnamacharya Yoga Mandiram make the findings of this study impossible to generalize to other settings. Typically, the findings in qualitative research are not intended for generalization to a larger population. Instead, qualitative research aims to contribute to a fuller understanding of what constitutes reality for the informants in a particular real-life setting (Morse, 1992). But the KYM is clearly "one of a kind" because it was established specifically to further the healing work of T. Krishnamacharya. T. K. V. Desikachar, its founder and overseer during the first twenty years of its existence and growth, had almost daily contact with Krishnamacharya, his teacher and father, until Krishnamacharya's death in 1989. This direct link from Krishnamacharya to

Desikachar to the teachers at the KYM would be impossible to replicate. But the fundamental principles of this tradition are teachable, and the KYM is open to sharing them with yoga teachers and students from all over the world.

Supporting Evidence from Co-researcher's Observation of Classes

Several months before the principal investigator conducted the interviews, one member of the research team spent five weeks at the site, observing one-to-one therapy sessions, and recording her observations as they occurred. Her comments, made in the freshness of the moment, support a number of the themes that were gleaned from analysis of the interview data. Her impressions were particularly strong in two areas. One is the "supreme optimism and sureness conveyed by the teacher," common to all the sessions she observed. She noted, "I believe the teacher's absolute confidence in the prescribed course transmits to the students in a therapeutic way." That transmission seemed to result in the particular "mind-set of the student and his trust in the teacher." Further, "the enthusiasm and optimism of the teacher in the very first session sets the tone for the whole course."

This confidence on the part of the teacher, supporting the student's positive attitude toward his practice, no doubt stems from a number of sources. These may include the teacher's comprehensive training and exposure to many successful cases. Also, as revealed in the interview data, the teachers' experiences with their personal practice and overcoming their own health problems had a great impact on their faith in the process. In addition, and perhaps more important, the teachers' personal connection to the lineage of Krishnamacharya and the faith they have in the larger tradition transmits confidence. As a teacher expressed to a student, "The process is good, so don't worry. You are very well protected."

Another observation emphasized by the observing researcher was the skill with which teachers dealt with psychological issues in addition to the student's physical symptoms. She noted, "It seems to me they are master psychologists as well, spending a lot of time initially in talking/listening, observing family or mental attitudes that were not presented as the reason for [coming to the KYM]." Other points of observation include the teachers' "nimble" response to the students' changing condition and circumstances. Never did a course appear to have been planned ahead of time (other than the initial course planned by the consultant). The teachers did not determine what to teach in a given lesson until they saw and talked with the student and observed the current practice. Frequently one of the consultants on duty was called in to give input. The theme of simplicity and efficiency in the practices was also supported in the observing researcher's notes. She wrote, "In everything I have observed, less is more."

Supporting Evidence from a Case Report

The course sheets (stick figures illustrating the practice given in each lesson) kept on file at the KYM substantiate many of the findings of this study. The American teacher who was studying and teaching at the KYM and who became one of the co-researchers in this study shared an illustrative case. Also one of the 22 teachers interviewed, she made an important observation: "Looking at a case—just at what is [written] on paper—is certainly not a good review. It's just a small piece of what is really going on." The descriptive case report given below is taken from the transcript of her interview.

He came in and he had suffered severe depression and hepatitis. . . . He was a young guy, probably mid-twenties. He was on a lot of medication, and he slept all the time. He was tired all the time, and incredibly weak. [The consultant] had written out a preliminary course as part of the consultation and he spoke to me about it beforehand. He told me, "I have given you this person. You just do this [the planned practice]. Don't worry about it." I was still surprised [when I saw him]. I wasn't expecting the severity of his condition.

He clenched his hands all the time. He was incredibly stiff. His neck was always scrunched into his shoulders. And if I asked him to inhale or exhale, it was always a [big gasp], sort of jerky, very fast, very jerky. Almost anything I asked him to do—the simplest thing—just sitting and breathing, was difficult for him or made him tired. Or after three or four breaths he complained of his back hurting.

Interviewer: Did he talk much about himself?

No. . . . But he would complain a lot, physical complaints, just when I would think we were making progress. It felt like back and forth, like one week we would try him standing and then the next [class] he would say, "I just can't do it; it's too tiring." And we would go back to seated postures. It was really a tricky balance for me trying to find out what worked for him best—the correct balance of strengthening him, energizing him without over-tiring him, stretching him without injuring him. It was a good learning experience for me.

Interviewer: But he was giving you some positive feedback?

Oh yes. He was giving positive feedback. That was another interesting thing about him. He would complain—and I learned this after a while—but he was improving dramatically. Yet he would still say, "I'm not doing well, teacher."

Interviewer: When you say, "improving dramatically," what were you seeing?

Things like his breath for one. . . . He really liked *Om shanti, shanti,* and one of the things he said was, "Oh, this is a good one to say, isn't it, teacher, because it means peace, right?" And I talked to him a little bit. . . . "Yes, this one is very good for bringing peace." And so he associated it with peace, even though I hadn't put that association on it. I pretty much just tried to encourage where I could without imposing things on him. But [the chant] was very effective for him. . . . Without the chant, his exhale was [very short].

It took a long time of just slowly sticking with it, and of course, it was good for me in many ways. . . . At first I felt like I was not the right person to teach him; I didn't have enough experience. . . . I was so worried about hurting him or doing the wrong thing, and I was constantly checking with the teachers. And it took quite some time; it's been almost a year now since I started seeing him. . . . But now he is doing *vinyasas.* He wants to learn *surya namaskar.*

Interviewer: What kind of *pranayama* is he doing now?

Still extending exhale, generally. I introduced *nyasam* early because of his clenching. I thought it would help him open up a little bit with his breathing, or open up his hands if he did it with his *pranayama.* So he does that, which he really likes. He is doing *sitkari* with the teeth and tongue, which he likes. That was also good because he was so stiff in the neck and shoulders.

We've started talking more. . . . I noticed one day he came in with a brightly colored shirt and I complimented him on it, and he said, "Oh, you know, previously I would wear only white shirts because it was too much stress for me to think of what would go with it, and white goes with everything." He said, "Today I looked in my closet and I thought this looks like a nice shirt and I put it on." It's just little things like that. I noticed little changes in his hair and his glasses, and I could tell that he was getting over his depression. . . . And he was very proud to say that his sleep was very good and he was off his medication. But then he would say, "But I'm not doing well because I felt sick for two or three days and I couldn't do my practice." So he just needed a lot of encouragement along the way.

Interviewer: Maybe he is afraid if he gets too well, you won't see him again.

I thought about that. Because he was also a case where, as he got better, I said, "You are doing the practice great on your own; you can come less often. You can come in eight weeks." He said, "No, no, please, at least once a month." But now I take it as a really good sign that it has been more than a month this time. . . . But slowly he has become more independent. He has started taking meditation classes at a local community hall. Things like that. . . .

[In retrospect] I would say that the main point that has come out in the lessons with him was that he was very respectful of the teacher-student relationship. And he kept telling me how it was me who was inspiring him, which also was very new to me. I wasn't used to that. I was used to working with [westerners]. The more I got to know him, he would speak of how he was inspired by our classes . . . . He was very much, "Oh, thank you, teacher; yes, teacher."

When this student began his work at the KYM, he presented long-standing physical and emotional problems. Any therapy resembling a "normal" yoga practice was out of the question. The first courses given him appear designed to promote mental focus and to relax him, aiming to improve his ability to breathe more freely. The consultant who met with him the first time chose his teacher with care, apparently intuiting wisely.

This student showed respect for his teacher from the beginning. He practiced regularly at home except for a few days when he felt too ill. He expressed to the teacher that the practice made him feel better, and he indicated that it gave him hope for overcoming his difficulties. The intensity of his courses increased slowly over a period of several months. Sometimes the progression appeared to be "one step forward and two steps back," with the courses changing according to the needs at the time. By the time of the interviews, his health had improved dramatically, and he was able to do a relatively vigorous *asana* practice.

Throughout the months of teaching him, the teacher was guided and supported by the consultants at the KYM. She quickly sensed the manner in which she should relate to him—with tremendous encouragement and patience. In the beginning the teacher felt somewhat daunted by the complexity of this case. But as the relationship developed, her own confidence grew. She began to realize that the relationship itself was as much a part of his therapy as was his practice. There was some indication that this student felt attachment to her, but at the same time, he was growing in self-confidence and independence. The case became quite satisfying for the teacher. She commented to the interviewer that this individual became one of her "favorite students."

CHAPTER 7

The question we most commonly ask is the "what" question—what subjects shall we teach? When the conversation goes a bit deeper, we ask the "how" question—what methods and techniques are required to teach well? Occasionally, when it goes deeper still, we ask the "why" question—for what purpose and to what ends do we teach? But seldom, if ever, do we ask the "who" question—who is the self that teaches? How does the quality of my selfhood form or deform the way I relate to my students, my subject, my colleagues, my world? How can educational institutions sustain and deepen the selfhood from which good teaching comes?"
(From: Parker Palmer, The Courage to Teach: Exploring the Inner Landscape of a Teacher's Life)

When I began this study I wanted to probe more deeply into what is happening when a yoga teacher attempts to help an individual who seeks yoga because of some illness. Many of my own students had come for that reason, and many times—not always— we were successful in overcoming, or alleviating at least, a number of health problems. Often it has been a mystery to me why a case turned out the way it did, successful or not. Often it has been difficult for me to determine if, when deciding what to do with a student, I had acted on hunches or on more rational decision-making. Although much more is clear to me now than at the beginning of my teaching, the process is still not without mystery.

The findings of this study confirmed for me much that I have understood about what a yoga therapist in this tradition does with a student. The themes developed in chapters 2 and 3—Tailoring the Teaching to the Individual Student, and Aiming at the Mind While Dealing with the Body—are comfortably familiar. But the theme and sub-themes in chapter 4 concerning these teachers' commitment to and identification with the KYM are a little unsettling to me as a westerner, reminding me once more of the vast cultural differences between India and my own country. The theme of chapter 5—Healing Through Relationship—reinforced what I have always known in my heart if not in my head. Taken together, chapters 4 and 5 have emphasized for me that yoga therapy will not be defined by a set of techniques. Yoga therapy, I believe, is more about the identity and integrity of the teacher somehow unlocking another person's potential to be well and whole.

Working on this project has led me to ponder the question above, phrased by Dr. Parker Palmer: "How does the quality of my selfhood form or deform the way I relate to my students, my subject, my colleagues, my world?" (p. 4). And to paraphrase this insightful and spiritually oriented educator, how can yoga teachers and therapists sustain and deepen the selfhood that enables them to aid another person's healing? Teachers at the KYM expressed repeatedly that their connection to the tradition that is the source of their teaching had everything to do with themselves as teachers. Their own study and practice, their training to teach, their on-going learning in this dynamic tradition of healing, and the availability of their teachers—shape every dimension of their work as yoga therapists. Stated in a nutshell, "We cannot be the teachers we are without seeing the teachers in front of us."

What does this mean for yoga teachers in the west where history is brief and culture is so different from that in India? I asked a similar question, rather off-handedly, to two of the teachers as we were ending their interviews. One of them told me about the counsel she had given to one of the foreign teachers studying at the KYM. The young woman did not know whether or not she should go back to her country and teach. The counsel given her was essentially, "Listen to your heart, keep your mind open, and trust that you are going in the right direction."

She said, "I don't know whether I am making the right decisions . . . . have I learned enough?" I said, "See, that doubt that you have, all of us still have. When we are with [Desikachar] now with his classes, I always feel: Have I learned enough? Am I taking what he is giving me? He is spending such a lot of time with us. But I'm not able to [grasp] what all he says.

So it's not enough; I have to put in more. . . . It is a process of learning. . . . But you are going in the right direction. Something in you brought you here. . . . When you have doubts, listen to your heart. It will guide you. Don't work from your head; work from your heart. All this observation and all that, it might be mind-boggling for you right now, but when you start teaching, it will be of great help to you."

When I heard the word, *Athayoganusasanam,* that first day [in the Diploma program], I was scared. I thought, "What is this word? And [Desikachar] is talking on this for two classes, and I don't understand." But as I started teaching, I was able to understand. . . . So I said to her, "Keep your mind open. Now it is all information for you. Store it in your floppy and bring it out whenever you want it. And when you start teaching, everything will come to you and help you." . . . And she asked me, "Should I stay [longer], or should I go back?" I said, "This decision is yours; others cannot make it for you. And once you take a decision for yourself, don't regret it or [worry] about it. For that to happen, you have to listen to your heart."

The other teacher responded to my concern about whether or not it is possible to apply an Indian model to an American environment. He referred to the concept of *viniyoga,* as found in the *Yoga Sutra.* He, too, reiterated the theme of faith and commitment.

The *Yoga Sutra* tells very clearly. Number one, be yourself, not some other person. If you are yourself in your own country, there will be no problem. If you are trying to be some other person from some other country, then the problem comes. . . . *Viniyoga* says, when you [deal with] a person, take into consideration these points—where he is living, what he is doing, what is his psyche. You see, an Indian psyche is not an American psyche. . . . Anybody who is a teacher, whether this country or any other country, if he does to suit the local conditions, they will learn it. But not to impose this on to that. It will not work at all.

I feel that with genuineness in whatever you do, even mistakes will be taken care of. Something may come to help you at the right time. All these things happen. . . . When there is a strong commitment, you find things you never thought would help will suddenly start helping you. So some higher force is at work, definitely.

APPENDIX

METHODOLOGY

T he intent of this study was to document the processes of yoga therapy as practiced by teachers at the Krishnamacharya Yoga Mandiram in Chennai, India. The study is essentially interpretive, seeking to describe phenomena that are complex and difficult to separate from each other. It aims to seek out and elucidate the subjective meanings given to events and circumstances by informants in the study. Interpretive methods are particularly appropriate for studying aspects of health and healing that are social and behavioral in nature and that display complex interactions (Lincoln, 1992).

Yoga therapy is "social and behavioral in nature, with complex interactions." How something is done and how the individuals involved feel about it are often more important that what is done. How things happen cannot be separated from the results obtained. Qualitative (interpretive) inquiry, that is, collecting and analyzing subjective, narrative data, is highly appropriate in studying such processes. Depicting process requires detailed description; the experience of process typically varies for different people; process is fluid and dynamic; and participants' perceptions are a key process consideration (Patton, 1990, p. 95).

Miller and Crabtree (1994) argue that the strength of qualitative research in clinical settings is its capacity to make explicit the underlying assumptions and beliefs that guide clinical practice, and to answer questions that "concern experience, meaning, patterns, relationships, and values" (p. 343). This study employed an interpretive approach to examine the processes associated with yoga therapy at the Krishnamacharya Yoga Mandiram. The study site is described in Chapter 1.

Study Participants

Twenty-two teachers, 13 women and 9 men, were interviewed in private, tape recorded sessions. The only criterion for selection of interviewees was that the individual be currently teaching at the KYM. Teachers at the KYM who were not interviewed were omitted only because of scheduling difficulties during the limited time the researcher was on site. Years of teaching experience ranged from one to 30 with a mean of 6 years and median of 8 years. Ten of the teachers served as consultants (senior teachers who meet each new student and oversee the assigned teacher's work) as well as teaching their own students at the KYM. Ages of the interviewees ranged from 24 to 63 with a mean age of 41.5.

Eleven of the interviewees had completed the KYM's Diploma training program. Six were currently in their internships in the program, one was well established as a teacher before the Diploma program was initiated in 1984, and four were in a subsidiary training program for individuals who were not granted a seat in the Diploma program.

Data Collection

Three American yoga teachers, each having studied previously at the KYM, constituted the research team. Data collection included private interviews with current teachers at the KYM, observation of consultations and therapy sessions over a period of several months, examination of records documenting therapy sessions, and observation of case study presentations for international students attending workshops at the KYM.

Each of the 22 participants in the study gave informed consent and was interviewed in one 45 to 60 minute private session over a period of two weeks. All interviews were conducted, tape recorded, and transcribed by the study's primary investigator. Interviews were loosely structured, varying according to the informants' background and experiences. The interviewer asked the informants to tell about the circumstances leading to their connection with the KYM as well as their training and preparation to teach. Each was asked for stories of their work with particular students, and their insights regarding yoga therapy.

A second member of the research team secured permission to observe 24 individual therapy sessions over a five-week period during the year prior to the interviews. A range of health problems were addressed in those sessions including alcoholism, asthma, back pain, diabetes, depression, hypertension, knee pain, multiple sclerosis, neck pain, obesity, and sinus congestion. The researcher recorded her observations following each session and obtained copies of most of the practice courses given to the student by the teacher. She also had opportunity to discuss with the teacher some of the issues needing clarification.

The third member of the research team had the unique position of both studying and teaching at the KYM for a period of several months, under the guidance of the senior teachers. She was one of the teachers interviewed and could give both an insider's and an outsider's perspective. In addition, she contributed detailed notes on all the therapy sessions she had observed and conducted during her tenure at the KYM.

Data Analysis

Analysis of the data followed a general protocol for inductively analyzing qualitative data. An inductive analysis is one in which interpretations are drawn from the particulars collected in the data. Data are not sought for evidence to prove or disprove predetermined hypotheses. Topics and themes for interpretation come from the data themselves, rather than being imposed at the beginning of the study. In this study, analysis of the data began with the interviewer transcribing the tapes and making notations concerning expression. Repeated reading of each transcription allowed the researcher to become thoroughly familiar with the data while obtaining a sense of the whole.

The next step in the analysis was to delineate and code all meaning units throughout the interview transcriptions. A meaning unit is a segment of the narrative that retains its meaning even when encountered out of its context (Tesch, 1990). Related meaning units were clustered into categories representing preliminary themes in the data. The process was recursive, that is, the researcher repeatedly went from transcription to theme and back to transcription in order to retain the context and the meaning intended by the participant.

Analysis within cases and across cases was used to seek evidence of patterns in the processes associated with yoga therapy and regarding the nature of the interactions between the teacher and student. Ultimately, the analysis resulted in four over-arching themes, each with constituent themes and descriptive illustrations.

Ensuring the Trustworthiness of the Study

Trustworthiness in an interpretive study means that the findings are true to the informants' intentions. Efforts by the investigators to ensure the trustworthiness of this study include: approaching each participant with genuine respect, thereby contributing to a climate of trust; maintaining a non-judging view of experiences observed and described in the interviews; explication of the social and cultural context of the study; verbatim transcription of the interviews; intensive involvement with the material; maintaining a thorough paper trail so that decisions and coding procedures are documented; and grounding the interpretations, that is, linking abstract concepts with concrete descriptions taken directly from the text.

Additional means were used to validate conclusions drawn by the researchers. Examination of records documenting student assessment, the practices given to the student, and changes in the student's health status, yielded substantial verification. Notes on observations of consultations, individual lessons, and informal conversations with teachers yielded more supporting evidence. The three researchers' individual roles in the project coalesced into a unified depiction of the process of yoga therapy at the KYM.

REFERENCES

Desikachar, T. K. V. with Craven, R. H. (1998). Health, Healing and Beyond. New York, NY: Aperture.

Desikachar, T. K. V. (1995). The Heart of Yoga. Rochester, VT: Inner Traditions International.

Desikachar, T. K. V. (1987). *Patanjali's Yogasutras.* New Delhi: Affiliated East-West Press Private Limited.

Feurerstein, G. (2001). Yoga therapy: Further ruminations. International Journal of Yoga Therapy, 11, 5-6.

Feuerstein, G. (2000). Toward a definition of yoga therapy. International Journal of Yoga Therapy, 10, 5-10.

Lincoln, Y. S. (1992). Sympathetic Connections between qualitative methods and health research. Qualitative Health Research, 2 (4), 375-391.

Miller, W. L. and Crabtree, B. J. (1994). Clinical research. In N. Denzin and Y. Lincoln (Eds.), Handbook of Qualitative Research (pp. 340-352). Thousand Oaks, CA: Sage Productions.

Morse, J. M. (1992). Phenomenology. In J. Morse (Ed.) Qualitative Health Research (pp. 91-92). Thousand Oaks, CA: Sage Publications.

Palmer, P. (1998). The Courage to Teach. San Francisco: Jossey-Bass Inc.

Patton, M. Q. (1990). Qualitative Evaluation and Research Methods (2nd Edition). Newbury Park, CA: Sage Productions.

Taimni, I. K. (1961). The Science of Yoga. Wheaton, IL: The Theosophical Publishing House.

Tesch, R. (1990). Qualitative Research: Analysis Types and Software Tools. New York: The Folmer Press.

Walach, H., Jonas, W., and Lewith, G. (2002). The role of outcomes research in evaluating complementary and alternative medicine. Alternative Therapies in Health and Medicine. 8 (3), 88-95.

GLOSSARY

Apanasana:
A lying pose in which the knees are drawn toward the chest, compressing the lower abdomen

Asana:
posture or pose

Asatya:
Wrong communication through speech, writings, gestures, or actions

Athayoganusasanam:
The first *sutra*, translated as "Here begins the authoritative instruction on yoga."

Atman:
The self

Ayurveda:
Traditional Indian system of medicine

Bhavana:
Attitude

Bhujangasana:
Cobra pose

Dharma:
Duty

Dvipadapitham:
Two-footed pose

Karma:
Action

Nyasam:
A finger technique

Patanjali:
The ancient sage believed to have codified yoga resulting in the *Yoga Sutra*

Pranayama:
Regulated breathing technique

Purusa:
Source of consciousness; perceiver

Rama:
Name of an Indian God

Salabasana:
Locust pose

Sarvangasana:	Shoulderstand
Satya:	Right communication through speech, writings, gestures, or actions
Sitali:	A technique for *pranayama*
Sitkari:	A technique for *pranayama*
Surya Namaskar:	A sequence of poses collectively called salute to the sun.
Sutra:	A statement free of ambiguity, full of essence, universal in context, and with few words.
Tadasana:	Mountain pose
Vinyasa:	A course of *asanas* progressing appropriately toward a desired goal
Viniyoga:	The concept of proper application, according to the circumstances
Yoga Sutra:	*Patanjali's* classic text on yoga